These are all the letters of the alphabet.
They are divided into three fami
Trace over them with your finger

C000044094

Tall letters.

b d f h k l t

g j p q y

Letters that sit with their
tails hanging down.

Small letters on the ground.

a c e i m n o r s u v w x z

Look again at the small letters.
Say their sounds and match them to the correct picture.

Trace over the letters with your finger.
Talk about the pictures.

Draw a circle round each **a** and each **o**.

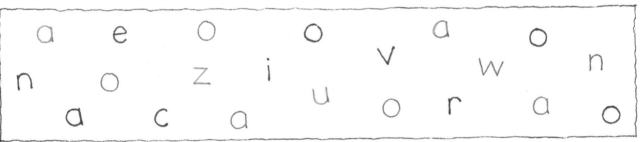

```
a    e    o    v    a    o
        a        i        w        n
n    o    z        v        n
n    a    c    a    u    o    r    a    o
```

Writing. Draw over the dotted lines.

Trace over the letters with your finger.
Talk about the pictures.

Draw a circle round each c and each s.

Writing

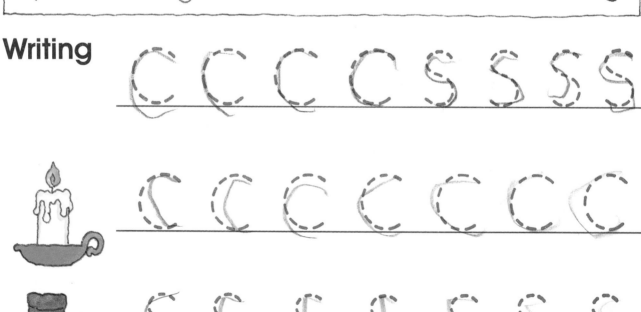

Trace over the letters with your finger.
Talk about the pictures.

Draw a circle round each i and each u.

i   i   e   i   u   u   u   i

   w   i   s

u   u   o   i   v   u   z   e

Writing

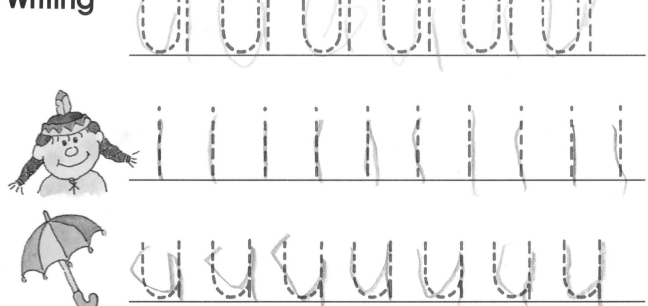

Trace over the letters with your finger.
Talk about the pictures.

Draw a circle round each **r**, **n** and **m**.

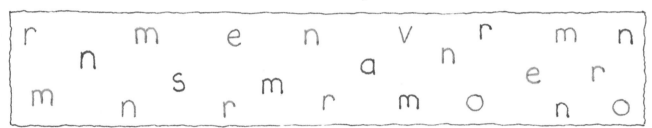

r		m		e		n		v		r		m	n
	n		e						n					
m			s		m		a					e		r
	n			r		r		m	o			n		o

Writing

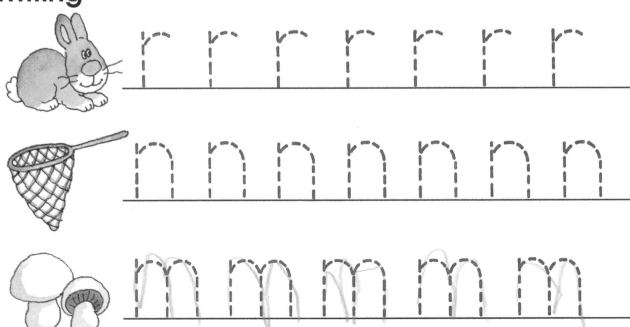

r r r r r r r r r

n n n n n n n n n

m m m m m m m m

Do the same on this page.
Talk about the pictures.

Draw a circle round each **v** and each **w**.

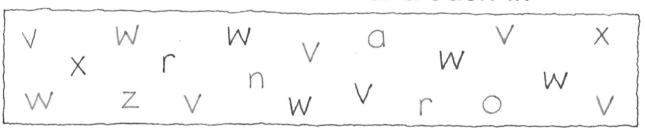

v   w   w   v   a   v   x

x   r   v   w

w   z   v   n   w   v   r   o   w   v

Writing

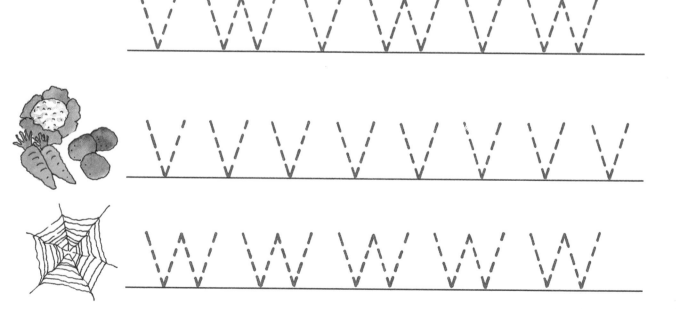

Trace over the letters with your finger.
Talk about the pictures.

Draw a circle round each x, e and z.

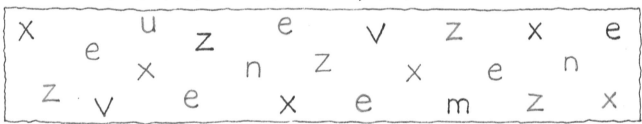

x u e v z x e
e z
x n z x e n
z v e x e m z x

Writing

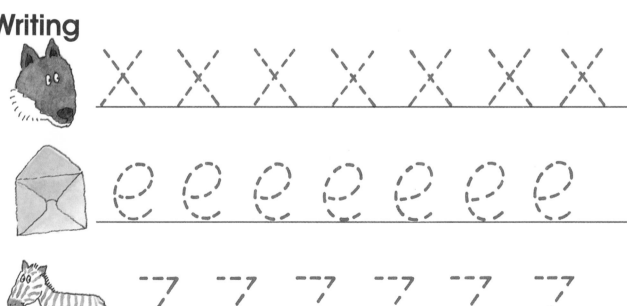

Here is the alphabet again.
Colour only the small letters.

Now find two small letters that match.
Colour them the same colour.
Use a different colour for each pair.

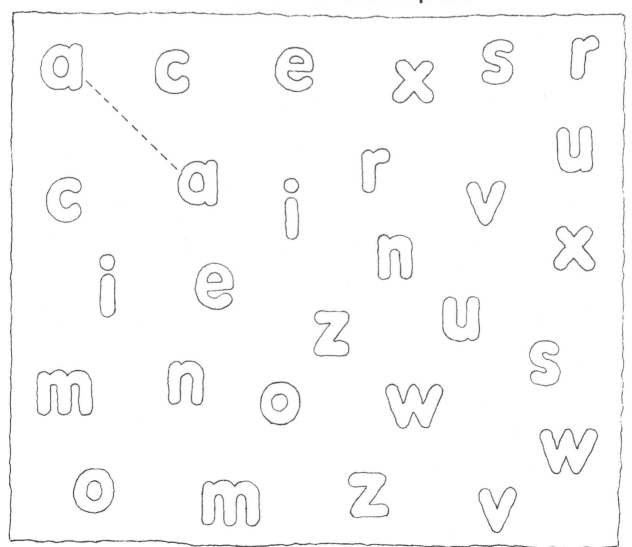

Here again are the letters that sit with their tails hanging down.
Trace over them with your finger.

Count the flowers. ☐   Count the butterflies. ☐

Count the birds. ☐   Find the ladybird! ☐

Finger first! Then talk about the pictures.

Draw a circle round each **g** and **q**.

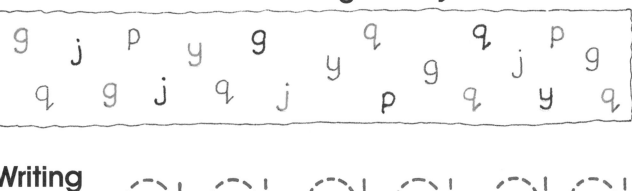

g   j   p   y   g   q   q   p
        j   y   q   j   g
q   g   j   q   j   p   q   y   q

Writing

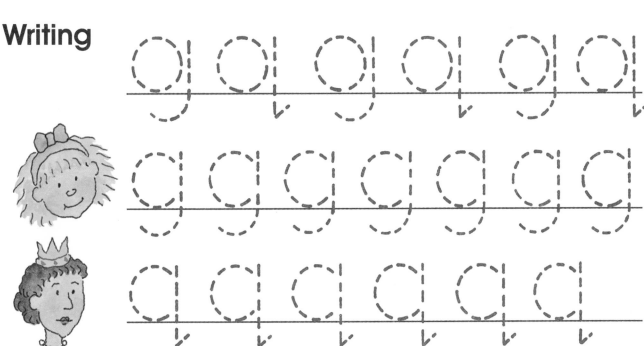

Finger first and this time, **you** colour the pictures.

Draw a circle round each **j**, **p** and **y**.

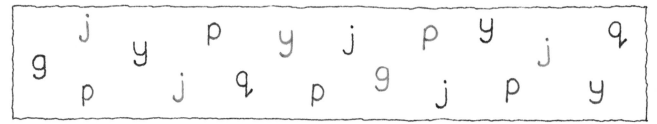

g j y p p y j p y j q
p j q p g j p y

Writing

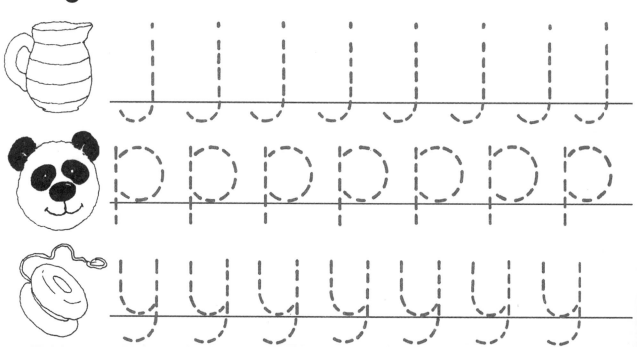

Here is the alphabet.
This time colour the letters with tails.

Match the tail letters that are the same.
Can you match the pair to the correct picture?
Look back in the book to see if you are right.

Do you remember the tall letters? They reach up high like the giraffe on page 1.
Trace over the letters with your finger.
These hot air balloons are high in the sky.
Say the sounds of the letters.

Finger first! Then talk about the pictures.

Draw a circle round each l and each k.

l   b   K   l   d   l   t   K   l   l   f   k

K   l   h   K   l   d   K   l

Writing

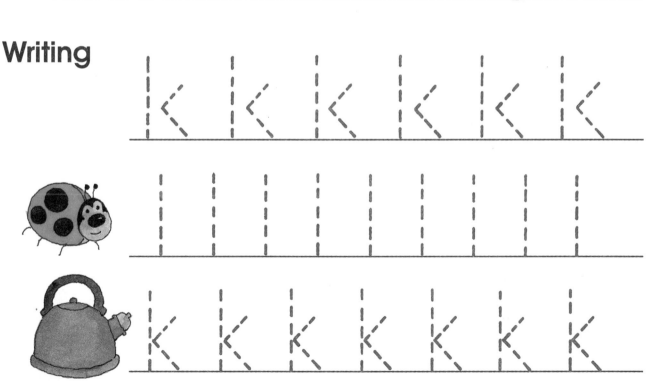

On both these pages draw over the letters with your finger then talk about the pictures.

Draw a circle round each **b** and each **h**.

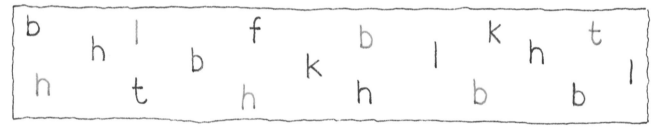

Writing bhbhbh

bbbbbb

hhhhhh

Draw a circle round each **f**, **d** and **t**.

f   l   d   k   l   d   t   f

t   d   t   f   d   t   l   f   k   d   h

Writing

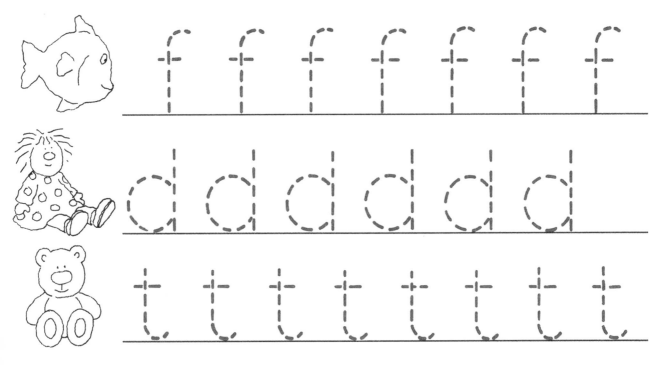

This is the alphabet again.
This time only colour the tall letters.

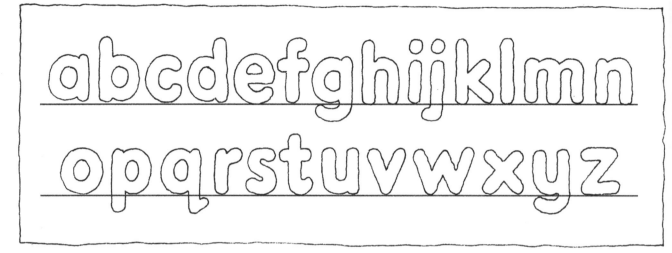

Match the tall letters and colour the shape so
that each pair of letters is in the same colour.

These are very special letters called **vowels**.

Draw a circle round all the letters . . .

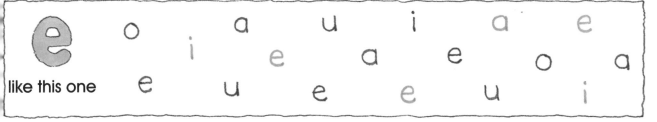

a
like this one

a		a		e		i		a		e	
	u				a		u				i
e		a	u		i	e		a		a	

e
like this one

	o		a		u		i		a		e	
		i		e		a		e		o		a
e		u		e		e		u		i

i
like this one

u		a		o		i		a		o	
	i		e		a		u		i		a
e		u	i	i		e	i	e		i	i

o
like this one

a		o			e		u		i	e
	u	i		o			a				
	i		e	i	o		o		o
o		o		a		o		e		a	

u
like this one

e		i		u		i		o		u		e
	u			e		a		i			
a		o	u		u		u		e		i

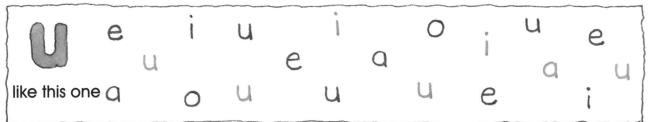

Practise writing.
Draw on top of the dotted lines.

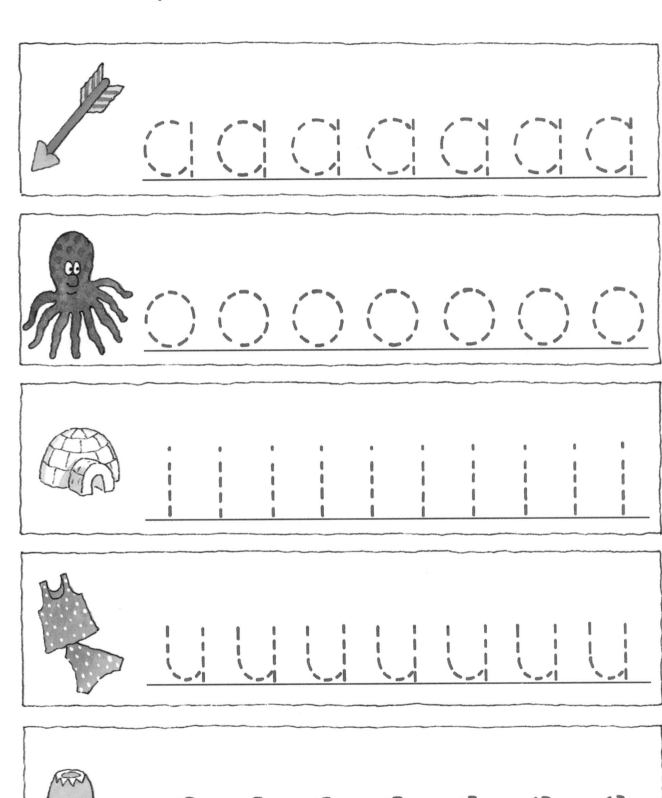

You've practised the small letters called vowels **a e i o** and **u.**

Now practise writing the other small letters.

c

m

n

r

s

v

w

x

Now practise the tall letters.

 b _____

 d _____

 f _____

 h _____

 k _____

 l _____

t _____

Practise again the letters with tails.

j

p

g

q

y

Now that you have practised all the letters of the alphabet, see if you can write your first name.

Ask a grown up to write it here.

_____

Now you write.

_____

_____

_____